The **WIND** Has Scratchy Fingers

The WIND Has Scratchy Fingers

by

Eth Clifford and Raymond Carlson

Educational Consultant: LEO FAY,
Professor of Education, Indiana University

FOLLETT PUBLISHING COMPANY · CHICAGO

*"Path of flame." Sunset
after an Arizona storm.*

1 ʕ ʕ ʕ ʕ

WE cannot see the wind, but it is everywhere. We cannot reach out and grasp it, yet it touches us every day of our lives. For millions of years, the wind has swept across the earth, whipping the seas, picking up and whirling particles of dust and sand before it.

The surface of the earth has been affected by many things over the centuries. We see the work of water erosion in valleys and gorges. We see it in the fantasy of the shapes of cliffs and rocks.

We see the work of the wind in a sunset, in a summer storm, in wheat rippling in the prairies, in the rustling leaves whirling to the ground in a rush of color on an autumn day. We see it in the swirling patterns of desert sands.

We are affected every day of our lives by the motion of wind. Imagine how our lives would be changed if the air stopped moving suddenly —the terrible heat of the tropics would make life impossible; the unrelieved cold in northern areas would freeze the land; the large cities of the world would be covered by clouds of fumes from factories and industry.

Fortunately, air is in constant motion. Wind is air moving horizontally along the surface of the earth, and it is the heat of the sun that makes air move.

"Lake breeze." A gentle wind makes ripples on the water.

The sun's warmth varies from season to season. In the northern hemisphere, summer days are warmer than are winter days. In December, the sun shines for about nine hours on a clear, bright day. Then, as winter gives way to spring and spring to summer, the days grow longer. By midsummer, the sun shines almost fifteen hours each day. And the longer the sun shines, the warmer the day.

Although a sunny day in winter is usually very cold, it is not because the sun gives off less heat; it is because the rays of the sun that reach us are slanted. They are weaker when they reach us, too, for slanted rays travel a longer distance through the atmosphere around the earth.

So we see that the rays of the sun are more direct in summer. In winter, the rays are spread out. Also, the slanted rays hit clouds, dust and smoke. They lose some of their energy and cannot give as much heat.

Many things cause variations in the temperature of the earth's surface. Not only winter and summer temperature differences, but also darkness and light affect the warmth of the earth.

Too, the heat of the sun is not absorbed in the same amounts by land as it is by water. Soil absorbs heat more quickly than water, but the rays of the sun do not pass far below the surface of the land. When the surface becomes warm, the air above it becomes warm, too.

So, when cold air moves in, it pushes the warm air upward. This movement of cold air pushing warm air is wind.

The further away from the earth's surface, the cooler the air. We find that the air over the equator, which rises and spreads, is warmer than other air. It should rise directly toward the poles. But the earth, as we know, turns on its axis. As it turns, it changes the direction of the moving air currents.

"Cottonwoods at sunset." A moderate wind moves tree branches.

Then the air does not go upward, but is turned from the poles. The moving air, which should be going north or south, now begins to go east and west. Because of the earth's rotation, all wind moving toward the equator moves west. All wind moving toward the poles moves east.

World-wide air movements are called planetary winds. According to the areas in which they blow, the planetary winds are called trade winds, prevailing westerlies and polar easterlies.

It is important to remember that winds are always named for the directions from which they come, not the directions toward which they go. That is why a wind which blows east is called the west wind. It comes from the west.

We know that air has substance, like wood or water. Air can be hot or cold. And it can be measured. At sea level, the atmosphere weighs 14.7 pounds per square inch, or enough to raise a column of mercury in a barometer to a height of 29.92 inches.

As far back as the days of Galileo, a young scientist named Torricelli took a single length of glass tube and made it airtight by sealing one end. Then he used a pump to suck out the air in the tube and closed the open end with his thumb. Quickly, he placed the tube over a bowl of mercury so that the sealed end pointed straight up. Then he removed his thumb from the tube.

The mercury in the bowl rose up into the empty tube. Torricelli decided that it could only have been air pressure that drove the mercury upward, for there was certainly no air in the tube. This crude tube was our first barometer.

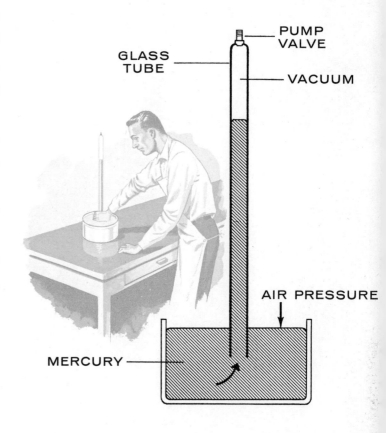

Torricelli's Experiment

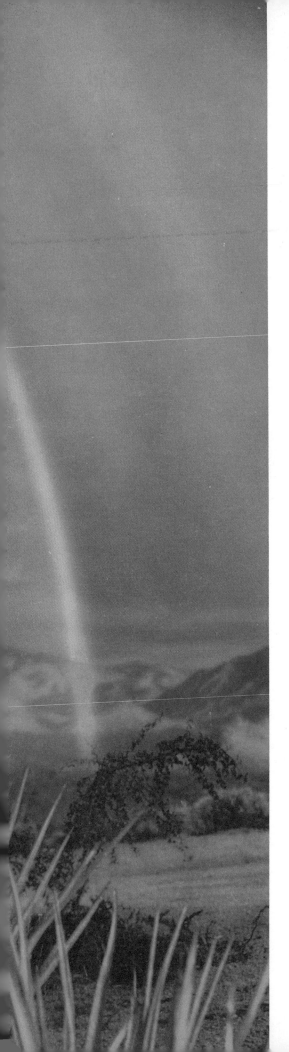

The earth moves through space, rotating as it moves. Around the earth, there is a shell of gas which we call atmosphere. This atmosphere goes hundreds of miles beyond the surface of the earth. Scientists divide it into areas based on its electrical and physical characteristics.

The first or lowest layer of air, which is closest to the surface of the earth, is called the troposphere. It goes up about eleven miles at the equator to about four miles near the poles. It is here that the storms, clouds, rain and snow are found. The troposphere is higher in the summer than in winter, and higher when the surface pressure is high than when it is low.

Above the troposphere, there is another layer called the stratosphere. Here, the air is cold and clear, thin and dry. Above this layer there is an area called the ionosphere, which goes hundreds of miles up into space.

The word troposphere is taken from a Greek word, *tropo*, which means "turning." It was given this name to describe the turning or overturning of the air due to moving currents created by temperature changes.

The troposphere has a "ceiling," called the tropopause, which is a thin layer of air that acts as a cushion between the stratosphere and our own stormy troposphere.

We can smell the wind. We can feel the wind. We can hear the wind. We can see what the wind can do. The names of the winds, as de-

"Desert rainbow heralds the storm."
The Mazatzal Mountain Range forms
an Arizona background for a rainbow.

· 10 ·

scribed by weathermen, are based on the Beaufort scale of winds. This system was first developed by a British admiral, Sir Francis Beaufort, in 1806.

When the weatherman describes the wind as calm, it is moving at a rate of less than one mile per hour. Smoke from a chimney will rise in a direct line toward the sky.

At one to three miles per hour, the smoke begins to drift gently, but the weather vane does not stir. This is termed "light air."

At four to seven miles, the wind is called a light breeze. Leaves rustle in the trees, and the touch of the wind on one's face is very pleasant.

A gentle wind moves eight to twelve miles an hour and will whip a small flag straight in the air. When it increases to thirteen to eighteen miles, the wind is described as moderate, but dust and paper on the road begin to whirl about and small branches move.

In a fresh wind, nineteen to twenty-four miles per hour, little waves stir the surface of a lake and small trees begin to sway. In a strong wind, twenty-five to thirty-one miles per hour, it is difficult to use an umbrella. Wires begin to hum with the sound of the wind.

Gale winds go from moderate at thirty-two miles per hour, to whole gales at sixty-three miles per hour. Storm winds blow from sixty-four to seventy-two miles per hour. Beyond that, the wind is of hurricane force, and is a savage instrument of destruction in the land.

"Cloudburst and rolling hills." A storm builds up over the Santa Rita foothills in southern Arizona

IF you have ever looked at dust particles in a shaft of sunlight, you may have noticed how very fine this dust appears to be. The wind lifts even finer particles of dust from dry fields and from the desert. It whirls the dust around the world and sometimes lifts it up as high as the stratosphere.

Usually, we do not see dust. Yet when we look at the splendor of a sunset, what we see is color caused by dust particles which scatter and disperse the sunlight. When the sun sinks from sight and the pinks of the sunlight deepen to purple, lingering even after the sun is no longer visible, what we see are sun rays reflected by dust particles at a height of from six to twelve miles.

When volcanoes erupt, bits of ash are tossed high into the air, and the wind seizes this fine ash dust and circles it around the earth. This ash can create spectacular colors in the sky. Even the color of the sun seems to change.

The fine ash from a raging forest fire in Canada, carried by the west wind, once made the sun shining over Europe look blue. Space, the light of the sun, dust and the wind—these are the instruments of beauty in the skies above.

But dust is not always a vision of color in the

"Sunset over Eagle Rock Mesa."
A lonely, wind-swept plateau
stands alone in Monument Valley.

sky. When the wind moves across the land, and great dust storms sweep over tremendous areas of the country, dust hurled by wind can be a terrible and a frightening sight. Millions of tons of precious soil have been lost to man as a result of dust storms.

It is possible for the wind to create such havoc, because in dry areas the soil is helpless before the wind. There is no vegetation to hold the valuable soil fast. There is no moisture in the ground to bind it.

All dry fields are not a consequence of erosion by nature. A good part of erosion is caused by the carelessness of man.

Early in American history, the pioneers moved westward in search of good, fertile soil. There was so much land available that the farmers tilled the soil until they had destroyed its fertility. Then they moved on to richer fields. The United States was so vast that they did not realize that there could be an end to the richness of the land.

Ranchers often overstocked their herds. They permitted their cattle to graze constantly in the same areas. Sandy trails were created by the movement of the cattle. The close cropping of the grass and the pounding the land took from cattle hoofs resulted in man-made erosion.

The natural vegetation throughout much of the western United States is short grass, which makes the area ideal for raising cattle. After the first world war, there was a tremendous demand for beef throughout the world which American

"Crossing the Gila River." An Apache cattle drive in Arizona.

ranchers and farmers were anxious to supply. But wheat was not a product that could grow normally in this area of uncertain rainfall.

Because ranchers permitted their very large herds to overgraze and because wheat growers plowed under the grass which bound the soil, the vegetation which protected the soil was stripped from the land.

Then, in 1934, there was a severe drought. The wind, blowing across the Great Plains, found loose, dry soil to drive before it. It whipped the dust as high as the stratosphere. The skies were dark with dust as far east as New York.

The earth was stripped for thousands of miles, and a new expression was born to describe the destruction of millions of acres of land. From the Texas Panhandle to Saskatchewan in Canada, the area was called the Dust Bowl.

The soil of Texas, Oklahoma, New Mexico, Kansas, Nebraska, Montana and Wyoming could produce few crops. Families began to drift westward. They abandoned their land to the wind.

But not all erosion is helped along by man. All rock can be worn down by sand grains that are picked up by the wind and then blown against the rock, for example. And sand and clay, created by weathering, can be removed by the winds in such quantities that only boulders or plain bedrock remain to create what is called a "desert pavement." Natives of the Southwest are familiar with this kind of erosion. Wind and sand together have fought a common battle against the land.

*"In Chiricahua National Monument, Arizona." The effects of
erosion are evident on these towers, pinnacles and spires.*

Sand is composed of rocks so tiny that they
measure less than two millimeters in diameter.
Larger fragments are familiar to us as gravel.
Very fine grains of sand are silt or clay.

The story of the earth is written in stone, for
the crust of the earth is rock. Over the centuries,
water, ice and air, the agents of erosion, have
weathered the rock by breaking it into fragments.
Then the wind acts as a transporting agent by
carrying the fragments to other areas.

Sometimes water acts as an agent of transportation, too. Torrents of rain wash pieces of rock down from the mountains. Rivers sweep the pieces down into valleys and river beds. As the fragments roll, they break into smaller and smaller pieces. Many of the pieces of gravel crack and are worn down eventually into sand.

The face of the earth, over millions of years, has been shaped by the forces of erosion, by the action of rivers, of glaciers, of frost and of wind. And, since the world began, erosion has chipped away at the surfaces of the earth.

Frequent weather changes cause erosion processes that beat at rocks and mountains. Rocks crumble, and the wind blows the smaller fragments away.

What the wind removes from one place, it deposits in another. We have seen how it can carry dust from one part of the country to another. When obstructions hinder the movement of dust, it is piled into hills against bushes, fences or houses by the wind. In the same way, sand, swirled by wind, hits boulders, fences or small rises in the ground and begins to form hills. These hills, that may be either small or large, are called dunes.

The ripples that create such beautiful patterns across the desert are miniature sand dunes. But the dunes do not remain stationary, for the wind, by pushing almost continually against the windward, or windy, side, shifts the grains into new shapes and formations.

"Windswept yucca." White Sands
National Monument, New Mexico.

"Sand and cliff." The desert plateau regions of
the southwest carry the marks of the weather. The
wind moves sand dunes and claws at steep cliffs.
Where there is protection from the wind, strange
desert plants and grasses struggle to survive.

Grain by grain, the wind deposits sand on the windward side until a heap is formed. The grains do not rest there, however. The wind pushes the grains up the crest and down the slope on the leeward, or sheltered, side.

The shifting of sand dunes is not always visible, although one can see the wind blowing the sand. Yet dunes have been known to move as much as one hundred feet in a year's time.

Sand dunes vary considerably in size. They may be ripples or hills a few feet high. Sometimes, as in the Sahara Desert, they form mountains that are 600 to 1,000 feet high.

Little or nothing is usually done to stop the migration of sand dunes. But the movement of some dunes has been stopped by planting grasses with long, creeping roots or by building sand fences. When large, modern highways run through desert areas, sand fences are built to prevent the hills of sand from covering the hard-surfaced roads.

With the passing of each hour, the patterns on sand change. The fences themselves are often bent into odd shapes by new sand storms.

Some sand dunes are not only beautiful but are also said to "sing." It is claimed that a harp-like sound can be heard in the desert of the Sinai Peninsula in Egypt when great mounds of sand tumble downhill. In the Hawaiian island of Kauai, the sand is said to make a deep, sharp sound, almost like a bark, when moved by the wind.

Some people think that sand, when blown by the wind, makes a sound like a humming wire. One explanation for some of the unusual tones is that, when sand is damp, a film of moisture covers each grain, and vibrations are then set into motion quite easily.

"The sand fence." Built to keep sand dunes from covering highways, the sand fences are changed by each desert storm.

"Spider Rock, Canyon de Chelly, Arizona."

3 ·⟋·⟋·⟋·⟋

From its very beginning, our continent has undergone changes. More than half of it was covered by a sea at one time, hundreds of millions of years ago.

Geologists, reading the story written in the walls of the Grand Canyon, for example, can point to regions that were once covered by an ocean. Other walls indicate areas that were, long ago, sandy valleys or swamplands.

Changes in the face of the earth are still taking place today, for the earth does not remain the same, unchanged, even during short periods of time.

Weather is more than a spring rain, a cloudy day or a clean sweep of snow on country fields: Weather helps cause physical changes on the earth's surface.

Each time there is a shower, a storm or a flood, each time frost nips the ground, each time day changes to night, the earth also changes. The change may not be severe, it may not cause a flood or an earthquake, but it happens daily.

Weathering is a process that results in the breaking down of rock. Temperature and air pressure changes are a part of weathering. Heat and cold, snow and ice, rain and wind—all these are a part of erosion.

The warmth of the sun beats down on rocks, causing them to expand. Then night, which often brings frost, chills the rocks, causing them to shrink.

Day after day, night after night, the rocks expand and contract. If the difference in temperature is great, the rocks begin to crack, and water soaks into the new crevices. Then, during the winter, the moisture in the cracks freezes.

· 25 ·

"Totem Pole, Monument Valley, Arizona."

When spring and summer come, the ground begins to thaw, and the water melts. So there is a continuous process of freezing and thawing. Changes in temperature and its effect on water have accomplished the action of crumbling the rock. Rivers and wind will carry away some of the fragments.

Rocks, as they erode, change into new and sometimes fantastic forms. Often their coloring is so magnificent that they look as if an artist had painted them.

Rocks vary in color, but many people feel that the most spectacular formations are bright red or orange. Utah's Bryce Canyon, where the eroded rock cliffs are formed of clay, shale and limestone, is a fairyland of pink and red spires.

And yet these colorful walls and pinnacles were once a solid rock plateau. Over a period of thousands and thousands of years, weathering and the actions of rain and wind slowly and steadily eroded the surface of the soft rock until it was worn into its present amazing shapes.

But Bryce Canyon will not remain as it looks today. In the centuries yet to come, rain will continue to loosen the rock, and wind will continue to blast at the weakened, grainy surfaces, using the loose sand as a powerful and effective chisel. First, the thin spires in the upper layers of the pinnacles will disappear. Then we can only imagine what new formations will be seen next.

The coloring of rock structures is of interest to both viewers and scientists. Geologists have

"Bryce Canyon panorama." These vast rock cliffs in Utah are overwhelming evidence of wind and rain erosion.

"Blue Mesa—Petrified Forest National Monument." The great naturalist, John Muir, named this Arizona land "The Blue Forest" when he saw the colors that band its clay hills.

studied the composition of rocks, and have learned that rocks are composed of minerals. It is the minerals and the actions of the earth's atmosphere on the minerals that give rocks color.

In the Painted Desert of Arizona, for example, most of the rocks are coated with a substance called iron oxide. Iron oxide is formed when oxygen, always present in air, combines with the iron found in the earth.

The amount of iron oxide is not the same in all rocks. The different shades of reds and oranges vary with the quantity of iron oxide present in the rocks. And, of course, the colors seem to vary in hue considerably, depending on the time of day or evening that they are seen.

When you pick up a piece of wood and whittle away at it with your pen knife, your knife digs into a solid piece of wood. You are creating a new form out of a formless mass. In the same way, the wind picks up grains of sand and scratches away at solid rock surfaces.

Over the centuries, abrasive sand and wind have worn through the rock to create new forms. Spires, towers, monuments of stone that rise as high as 900 feet in the air, bridges, arches—these spectacular rock formations seem so permanent that it is easy to forget that they did not always exist as they now stand.

It is difficult to realize that all of these forms were created by the removal of rock or soil, that these wonders of nature are the work of erosion, and that they are changing constantly.

The same piece of wood, which you have whittled, now has shape, but is it finished to your satisfaction?

You run your fingers over the wood and find it rough to the touch. You decide to rub it with sandpaper. As you apply the sandpaper, over and over again, the wood begins to feel smooth. It begins to look polished.

In the same way, the wind can take grains of sand, millions of grains of sand, and blast forcefully against the rough surfaces of rock. Day after day, year after year, century after century, the wind scratches at the rock and wears away the surface. The rough surfaces now have a smooth and polished look. By wearing away the rock and then polishing it, the forces of nature have produced still another form of erosion.

To men of ancient times, the wind was a mystery to be feared, an impulsive messenger of the gods. They prayed to the wind and made sacrifices to tame it. From Biblical days to this moment, the wind has inspired men to write tales and poetry of its evil ways and its goodness.

We have come far since the early days of fear and ignorance. When we ask, "What is the wind?" we do not answer mysteriously, but scientifically. We know what it is, how it begins, how it affects the land. With the help of wind instruments, we can forecast future weather conditions.

This does not mean that modern man knows all the answers. The more man learns, the more he wishes to learn. There is still much he needs to know about the wind. But even modern man stands in awe of the wind's power and majesty.

"Wind-polished canyon walls." The imposing White House Ruins, Canyon de Chelly National Monument, Arizona.

GLOSSARY

abrasive (ə-brā'-siv), having a tendency to rub or wear away.

bedrock (bed'-rok'), the solid rock underneath the soil.

capricious (kə-prish'-əs), changeable; guided by passing whims and fancies.

characteristic (kār'-ik-tər-is'-tik), a special trait or quality.

consequence (kon'-sə-kwens), a result of an event.

considerably (kən-sid'-ər-ə-bli), much, to a great extent.

crevice (krev'-əs), a narrow, deep opening or crack.

crude (krüd), rough, unfinished.

deliberately (di-lib'-ər-ət-li), slowly, carefully, on purpose.

disperse (dis-pėrs'), to scatter, to go in many different directions.

eventually (i-ven'-chü-ə-li), finally, at last, at a later time.

film (film), a thin coating or surface, sometimes of a liquid.

havoc (hav'-ək), great damage and destruction.

hue (hū), a color or shading of color.

inspire (in-spīr'), to put life, strength or feeling into.

ionosphere (ī-on'-ə-sfēr), that part of the atmosphere beginning twenty-five to thirty miles out from the earth's surface and extending indefinitely toward outer space.

iron oxide (ī-ərn oks'-īd), iron exposed to oxygen that, in some rocks, results in bright shades of red, yellow and orange.

millimeter (mil'-ə-mē-tər), a very small unit of measure; about four hundredths of an inch.

moderate (mod'-ər-it), mild, not extreme.

obstruction (ob-struk'-shən), something blocking the way.

pattern (pat'-ərn), an example, model, guide.

pinnacle (pin'-ə-kəl), a tall, slender peak or point.

prevailing (pri-vāl'-ing), having superior force or influence; most frequent.

spectacular (spek-tak'-ū-lər), causing excitement or admiration by a great display.

stratosphere (strat'-ə-sfēr), that part of the atmosphere between the troposphere and the ionosphere.

strip (strip), to take away completely, as soil from the earth.

structure (struk'-chər), the way something is made or put together.

Texas Panhandle (teks'-əs pan'-han'-dəl), that narrow part of the state of Texas extending about 133 miles north of the upper Red River.

texture (teks'-chər), the softness or hardness of something; its coarseness or fineness.

till (til), to cultivate land, to plow.

tropopause (trōp'-ə-pôz), the upper part of the troposphere.

troposphere (trōp'-ə-sfēr), that part of the atmosphere closest to the earth.

undergo (un'-dər-gō'), to pass through, to suffer.

vary (vā'ri), to make small changes in; to differ.

vibration (vī-brā'-shən), a rapid movement back and forth, as a quivering.

Key to pronunciation: pat, āte, bāre, cär; red, mē, ėr; pit, mīne; cot, tōne, bôrder, choice, our; cut, ūse, put, rüle; thin, then. ə represents any unaccented vowel. A heavy mark (') follows the most strongly accented syllable in a word; a lighter mark (') follows a syllable with lesser stress.

Grateful credit is given to *Arizona Highways*, its editor, Raymond Carlson, and its staff for their assistance in producing *The Wind Has Scratchy Fingers*; to Tom Culver for the drawing which appears on page 9; and to the following photographers whose work appears in the book: Chuck Abbott, page 18; Robert E. Aherns, 23; Jack Breed, 20; Bob Clemenz, 31; J. Fred and Fran Dodson, 6; Esther Henderson, 2-3, 26-27; Hubert A. Lowman, 17; Ray Manley, 15, 24; H. H. Miller, 4; David Muench, 13; Josef Muench, front and back covers, 1, 8, 21, 25, 28; Willis Peterson, 10; and Mabel Weadock, 11.